El Greco

Fundación Amigos del Museo
del Prado

Floor plan of the Prado Museum

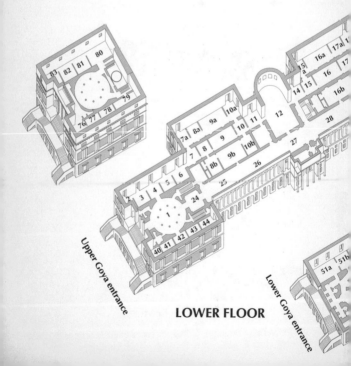

SECOND FLOOR

LOWER FLOOR

Upper Goya entrance

Lower Goya entrance

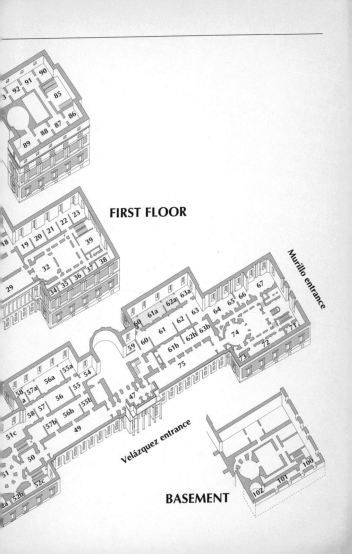

FIRST FLOOR

Murillo entrance

Velázquez entrance

BASEMENT

Second edition: 1999 (December)

Cover and interior design by Ángel Uriarte
Translation by Everett Rice
Axonometric projections by Ana Pazó Espinosa
Edition by Carmen Ponce de León and Manuel Florentín
Layout by Antonio Martín

© Fernando Marías, 1998
© Fundación Amigos del Museo del Prado
   ISBN: 84-922260-6-4
   Depósito legal: M -1563-2000
   Impreso en Varoprinter, S.A. C/ Artesanía, 17. Pol. Ind Coslada (Madrid)
   Printed in Spain

Introduction

Domenikos Theotokopoulos was born in 1541 in the city of Candia, capital of the island of Crete which at that time was a possession of the Republic of Venice. He was born into a Greek family who were probably Roman Catholic rather than Greek Orthodox and whose members worked for the colonial government. Although no one knows who might have been his teacher on the island, he must have been trained according to the dictates of late Byzantine tradition, and only partially assimilated some of the principles of the Italian Renaissance on his own. By 1563 he had already become a master painter and in 1566 we find him requesting appraisal of an icon of the Passion so that he could sell it in a lottery. By 1567 he seems to have moved to Venice, where he was to live until 1570. There, he may have been a pupil of Titian's, or rather learned the master's style without joining his studio. Eventually, Domenikos mastered the Western art of the Venetian Renaissance in his use of colour, perspective, anatomy and the technique of oil painting, even though he did not completely abandon his traditional manner. After a study trip through Italy (Padua, Vicenza,Verona,Parma,Florence) he settled in Rome where he would stay until 1576 or 1577.He came into contact with the intellectual circle of Cardinal Alessandro Farnese, who often received Spanish churchmen and men of letters, and he finally took lodgings in the attic of the Cardinal's palace. In 1572 El Greco was admitted to the Accademia di San Luca,the Roman painters' guild association, and may have opened his own workshop as a consequence.From then on, he worked primarily as a portraitist and painted small religious works for private clients in a much more advanced and Italianized style.Nevertheless, he must not have achieved much success as he decided to emigrate.

Although we are not sure of the reasons for his journey to Spain, we find him there in the spring of 1577. One hypothesis is that he was interested in entering the service of Philip II for the decoration of the Monastery of El Escorial. By the spring of 1577 El Greco was in Madrid, and from there he went to Toledo, where he was engaged by the Cathedral and the Convent of Santo Domingo el Antiguo and worked on the first canvases documented in Spain: the *Expolio* (Disrobing of Christ) for the Cathedral, and three altarpieces for the Convent church. El Greco was accompanied by a young Italian assistant named Francesco Prevoste, who lived and worked at the master's side until his death. In 1578, El Greco's son, Jorge Manuel Theotocópouli (the Italianized form of his surname), was born of an apparently ephemeral relationship with Jerónima de las Cuevas, who came from the artisan class of Toledo. From this moment on, 'El Griego' lived permanently in Toledo, leaving town only on rare occasions, and then only for professional reasons. His life was uneventful except for the lawsuits (we have documentation for nine) which were filed by him or against him by clients, either concerning the value or the price of his canvases, because of complaints about technique, or for iconographical reasons. Such was the case with the *Expolio* itself, or with the painting of *Our Lady of Charity* in Illescas at the end of his career. After Philip II and the Hieronymite congregation of El Escorial rejected his *Martyrdom of Saint Maurice,* which had been a royal commission intended for one of the altars of the basilica, El Greco enlarged his workshop and began the production of altarpieces — not just independent canvases — for the convents and parish churches as well as the archbishopric of Toledo. He also made smaller paintings for a private clientele. In any case, the bulk of his work consisted of the global execution of altarpieces for monasteries, parish churches, and chapels such as those of Talavera la Vieja (Cáceres), the Chapel of San José in Toledo, the Chapel of the Colegio de San Bernardino, the church of the Hospital of Our Lady of Charity in Illescas, the Ovalle Chapel in the parish church of San Vicente Mártir, or those of the Hospital of San Juan Bautista, or Tavera, which was left unfinished when he died. He was commissioned, sometimes with his son, for many others which he never managed to carry out, such as the important commission for the royal Hieronymite Monastery of Our Lady of Guadalupe (Cáceres). In some of these later commissions, El Greco often projected complete artistic settings in an innovative way: he would combine painting, sculpture, and the architecture of the altarpieces with other canvases fitted into walls or vaults, in order to create complex formal and visual systems which must have fascinated the spectators of his time (today it is difficult to find one of these projects in its original state). He made projects for sculpture and architecture, a discipline that interested him throughout his career in Spain. Even though he never actually designed a building himself, he was frankly opposed to the contemporary local postulates set down at court by the royal architect Juan de Herrera and faithfully imitated by Herrera's followers in Toledo.

El Greco lived in a refined environment, probably spending more than he earned, and was surrounded both by the academic and intellectual elite of Toledo and a small group of italianized and hellenized friends. He died on April 7, 1614. His work was praised by poets such as Luis de Góngora or the Discalced Trinitarian friar, Hortensio Félix Paravicino, and his paintings were collected by connoisseurs. El Greco enjoyed life, and he left behind the reputation of a man who was 'eccentric', peculiar, and paradoxical on account of his theoretical ideas and his highly personal and immediately recognizable style. His colleagues mythicized him for his attempts to raise the social standing of painters, but he was also criticized by the more intransigent theoreticians of the Counter-Reformation because of the liberties he took with form and iconography — be it the tone, the whole, or just a detail of a painting. They rejected his unbounded interest in what they considered to be the superfluous formalistic aspects of his work as well as his treatment of religious subjects which they found inappropriate from the most important functional point of view of the day: to incite the viewer to prayer, as determined in 1605 by the Hieronymite historian of El Escorial, Fray José de Sigüenza.

El Greco's art was repudiated by the 18th-century Enlightenment, but he was rediscovered by the Romantics and the French painters of the nineteenth century who interpreted it according to their own premises. Their interest in the work of Diego Velázquez caused them to take a new look at El Greco, who was his only truly original precedent in the history of Spanish painting. The Spanish Generation of 1898 saw El Greco as representative of the religious spirit of the Golden Age in Spain and closely related to the two greatest figures of the literary aspect of that spirituality: St. Teresa of Avila and St. John of the Cross. Early 20th-century painters saw El Greco as a precedent for their own expressionistic concerns — subjective, tormented, and unrestrained by a servile or mechanical imitation of reality.

Today, El Greco's work is undergoing a process of debate and reappraisal. His ties with Carmelite spirituality and his identification with Spanish values have been questioned. At this moment, greater emphasis is being placed on the Italian influence on his cultural and artistic development. The philosophical nature of his art is being stressed, with a focus on his interest in the formal, beautifying function of art as a means of understanding nature. Instead of being a model for mystical, impulsive artists, he is seen as an aesthete, an intellectual or philosophical painter, a 'genius' who was not involved in the concerns of his devout and erudite contemporaries. For some, El Greco voluntarily served the interests of the Counter-Reformation in the Spain of Philip II and Philip III for which he became a keen interpreter. For others, he kept his distance from such matters and, going against the current, concerned himself exclusively with the development of a very personal and formalistic kind of painting that was consistent with his own theoretical postulates about the nature of art. He recorded these ideas in personal annotations in some of the books in his library, mainly in the margins of Giorgio Vasari's *Lives* and Vitruvius's *De architectura*. This range of possibilities is a logical response to El Greco, who even in his own day was considered unusual and paradoxical. It also shows the interest that his work arouses among critics and historians of art and culture, just as it does among viewers who approach his paintings and experience the drawing power and the disconcerting impact of his work.

RELIGIOUS PAINTINGS

THE ALTARPIECE OF SANTO DOMINGO EL ANTIGUO

The Holy Trinity   Saint Benedict

THE ALTARPIECE FROM THE COLLEGE OF DOÑA MARÍA DE ARAGÓN

The Crucifixion   The Resurrection of Christ
Pentecost   The Baptism of Christ
The Annunciation

THE APOSTLE SERIES OF ALMADRONES

Saint James the Great   St. Thomas the Apostle or St. Philip
The Saviour of the World   Saint Paul

OTHER RELIGIOUS PAINTINGS

Saint Jerome as Penitent   The Virgin Mary
The Adoration of the Shepherds   Saint Antony of Padua
Saint John the Evangelist   Saint Paul
The Holy Face (Veronica's Veil)   Saint Andrew and Saint Francis
Christ Bearing the Cross   The Annunciation
The Coronation of the Virgin   Saint Sebastian

PROFANE SUBJECT

Allegory

PORTRAITS

The Doctor and Poet Don   Young Gentleman
    Rodrigo de la Fuente   A Gentleman
Gentleman with Hand on Chest   Trinitarian or Dominican Friar
Don Rodrigo Vázquez de Arce   A Gentleman
A Gentleman   The Jurist Don Jerónimo de
Don Julián Romero de las   Cevallos
    Hazañas and his patron
    saint, St. Julian

THE ALTARPIECE
OF SANTO DOMINGO EL ANTIGUO

In 1577, El Greco began his artistic career in Toledo with the commission to paint the *Disrobing of Christ* for the Cathedral, and to design three altarpieces, as well as to execute the accompanying paintings, for the main church of the Convent of Santo Domingo el Antiguo. He finished this work in 1579. The Cistercian nuns' new church, designed by the royal architect Juan de Herrera and built by the Toledan Nicolás de Vergara el Mozo, was to house the burial chapel of the noblewoman Doña María de Silva. In charge of these works was her executor, Don Diego de Castilla, dean of the Cathedral of Toledo and father of Don Luis de Castilla, whom El Greco had met in Rome. As existing records concerning his fees show, once El Greco had arrived in Toledo, the Dean offered him the contract for the altarpieces and paintings, which are centred on the subject of the Resurrection. The side altarpieces were dedicated to the "Adoration of the Shepherds with St. Jerome" — now in the Botín Collection of Santander — and the "Resurrection of Christ with St. Ildefonsus", still *in situ*. The main altarpiece had an enormous tabernacle that has since been lost. Above it were the paintings of the *Assumption of the Virgin* (Art Institute of Chicago), the *Holy Face* (now in Barcelona), and the *Holy Trinity* (Prado, Madrid), in the central vertical zone. Situated to the left of this central section were the images of *St. John the Baptist (in situ)* and *St. Bernard* (Russia), and to the right, *St. John the Evangelist (in situ)* and *St. Benedict* (Prado). Three gilded sculptures of the theological virtues of Faith, Hope, and Charity crowned the upper pediment; two others depicting Old Testament prophets finished off the upper ends of the altarpiece. The Prado Museum has two paintings from this altarpiece.

THE HOLY TRINITY (Cat. No. 824)

Originally set in the upper tier of the main altarpiece of Santo Domingo el Antiguo (1577-1579), El Greco's composition is based on a woodcut by Albrecht Dürer (1511) depicting the Trinity arranged as the 'throne of mercy', with God the Father sustaining the dead body of Christ on his lap, surrounded by angels bearing the symbols of the Passion. These instruments disappeared in El Greco's painting. Starting with Dürer's model, El Greco added several new elements, such as the anatomical and compositional treatment of the figure of Jesus, with clear references to Michelangelo's sculpture (the statue of Lorenzo de Medici and the *Pietà* in the Vatican). He also changed the papal tiara of the Father for a mitre, which was the typical headdress worn by the high priests of the Old Testament. The stylized beauty of Christ's body, in strong relief that emphasizes his weight, and the serenity of his face, lovingly contemplated by the Father, contrast greatly with the expressiveness and movement of the angels. In their elegance and strong colour, these angels form a kind of border around the principal image. This image is inundated with a supernatural light coming down from a golden cloud against which we can see the dove of the Holy Spirit. El Greco has changed the pathos and linear quality of Dürer's woodcut to serene tonalities, beautiful bodies, and a concept of naturalism that is based on the play of colour and light and the spiritualized movements of the figures. Acquired by Ferdinand VII in 1827.

Saint Benedict (Cat. No. 817)

Benedict was the founder of the Rule from which stems the Cistercian order of the Bernardine nuns of the Convent of Santo Domingo de Silos, called 'el Viejo' or 'el Antiguo' in Toledo. This half-length figure, with a matching *St. Bernard* (recently discovered to be in Russia), was set to the right of the central painting dedicated to the Assumption in the main altarpiece. It is a recurrent iconographical subject in the churches of this religious order. We see St. Benedict in full physical presence thanks to the obvious three-dimensionality of the figure. He stands out against a background of cloud effects, and

is wearing a black habit and cowl. He holds a founder's staff in his left hand, and uses his right to point toward the tabernacle which, lost today, was once a magnificent piece of open architecture. The tabernacle was set just below the image of St. Benedict and that of St. Bernard, to the left, who was seen more in full-face view and did not point towards the Blessed Sacrament in the tabernacle. Beneath these were two more paintings: on the left was St. John the Baptist, who pointed to the tabernacle with his right hand crossed over his torso; on the right was St. John the Evangelist meditating on the text of his Revelation, far removed from anything that might disturb his reading. This crisscross composition helped stress the Eucharistic significance of the altarpiece. St. Benedict looks directly out at the viewer, as an invitation to partake of the knowledge and worship of what the iconography of the whole altarpiece signifies. This painting came from the Museo de la Trinidad.

THE ALTARPIECE FROM THE COLLEGE OF DOÑA MARÍA DE ARAGÓN

The *Annunciation* in the Prado (on deposit until a few years ago in the Balaguer Museum, Vilanova i Geltrù, Barcelona), the *Adoration of the Shepherds* in the Museum of Budapest, and the *Baptism of Christ* in the Prado once formed part of the main altarpiece which was the iconographical and artistic centre of the church of the Augustinian College of the Incarnation in Madrid. This institution was popularly known as the College of Doña María de Aragón, from the name of its foundress. Before her death in 1593, Doña María de Córdoba y Aragón had been lady-in-waiting to Queen Ana, the fourth wife of Philip II, and to the Infanta Isabel Clara Eugenia, Philip's daughter by his third wife, Isabel de Valois. From that time on, the College was left in the hands of Hernando de Rojas, its second rector, and the executor of Doña María's will, Jerónimo Oraá de Chiriboga, canon of Talavera de la Reina. Both were men of dubious activities, especially the former, who was accused of engaging in witchcraft. Perhaps it was Jerónimo who, because of his Toledan origins, proposed El Greco for the paintings of the main altarpiece. But when a lawsuit was filed against Doña María's executors, it was to be the Royal Council of Castile who commissioned El Greco as the painter for this altarpiece in late 1596. He delivered the finished work around the middle of 1600, a year after the stipulated deadline and the inauguration of the church and Doña María's funerary chapel. The architecture of the church, which until our century had an elliptical rather than a Latin-cross shape, was traditionally attributed to El Greco, as well. In fact, we now know that it was designed by the royal architects, Juan de Valencia and Francisco de Mora. The altarpiece itself has been lost, but it may also have been designed by El Greco. The altarpiece and its paintings were once appraised at El Greco's behest by the painters Juan Pantoja de la Cruz and Bartolomé Carducci (or Carducho). The altarpieces for the two side altars, with images of St. Augustine and St. Nicholas of Tolentino (Prado Museum Cat. No. 1040 A and B), were left in the hands of the court painter and royal portraitist, Juan Pantoja de la Cruz (Valladolid, c. 1553-Madrid, 1608). They were commissioned in 1601, to complete the programme of the chapel with images of various Augustinian saints. Some critics have identified other paintings as once pertaining to El Greco's main altarpiece, but, so far, there has been no unanimity in accepting the various reconstructions that have been proposed. The most likely reconstruction places the Prado's *Crucifixion* in the centre of the upper tier. Yet another proposal reconstructs the altarpiece without this upper tier and adds the *Resurrection* and the *Pentecost* now in the Prado to the canvases already mentioned, despite the fact that the upper part of both of the Prado paintings has a semi-circular format. Whatever the original organization may have been, the altarpiece from the College of Doña María de Aragón was the most important commission that El Greco carried out in Madrid, and it was recognized as such from very early on. It was also to become the principal work of reference in El Greco's oeuvre — even more than his works in Toledo. For better or for worse, it would be analyzed and commented upon by critics and historians for years to come.

THE CRUCIFIXION
(Cat. No. 823)

The date of this signed canvas is still under discussion among specialists. Some of them maintain that the painting came from the parish church of San Juan Bautista in Toledo which, until their expulsion from Spain in the 18th century, had been the Professed House of the Jesuits in Toledo dedicated to St. Ildefonsus. Other experts say that the canvas must have been part of the attic of the altarpiece of the College of Doña María de Aragón in Madrid. Its iconography is absolutely exceptional in the oeuvre of El Greco. Christ is shown after his death on the cross, between two angels who are gathering the blood that flows from the wounds in his side and hands, and a third angel, incredibly and unnaturally foreshortened, who uses a cloth to wipe and dry the blood that falls from his feet. The representation is completed with the figure of St. Mary Magdalene at the foot of the Cross, and those of the Virgin Mary and St. John on either side. Equally exceptional is the depiction of Christ after his death rather than before it, and the positioning of his right foot on top of his left foot, against the

norm. This detail has been associated with the writings of the Blessed Alonso de Orozco, an Augustinian friar who inspired the foundation of the College and, indirectly, some of the details of the iconographical programme of its principal altarpiece. All of this seems to indicate that El Greco received detailed specifications from his clients — the Canon Don Jerónimo Oraá de Chiriboga and the Augustinian Fray Hernando de Rojas — and that he knew quite well how to integrate them into his highly personal concept of painting. This work came from the Museo de la Trinidad in the 19th century.

17

PENTECOST (Cat. No. 828)

As will be seen in the entry for the *Resurrection* (Cat. No. 825), this signed canvas has been linked to the main altarpiece of the College of Doña María de Aragón. It has also been paired with the *Resurrection* because of their similar size and shape. For stylistic reasons the *Pentecost* has been dated around 1605. In it we find a self-portrait of the artist as a grey, balding and bearded apostle who stares out at the spectator from the upper right-hand side of the canvas. The identification with El Greco is convincing because of the resemblance with his more youthful image in the *Purification of the Temple* (along with Titian, Michelangelo and Giorgio Giulio Clovio), now in Minneapolis, and with his *Self-portrait,* at the Metropolitan Museum in New York. The subject of the Coming of the Holy Spirit, in the form of tongues of fire which would grant the gift of tongues to the apostolic college, is quite exceptional in the oeuvre of El Greco. Even though it was not mentioned in the 18th century as one of the paintings hanging in the Monastery of Our Lady of Atocha in Madrid, this does not exclude that possibility. El Gre-

co's treatment of light, his strongly contrasting colour and generally dark tones, as well as the vital sense of agitation in the figures, which seem 'possessed' by the Holy Spirit, corresponds as much to the subject of the painting as to the artist's later style, of which this is a magnificent example.

THE ANNUNCIATION
(Cat. No. 3888)

This signed painting was kept in the Madrilenian College of Doña María de Aragón until the period of the *Desamortización* (Disentailment of monasteries) in the 19th century. It depicts the Incarnation, the central meaning of the Gospel episode of the Annunciation, as befits the advocation of the College itself. It stresses the moment of the Incarnation of the Son of God, the Word made flesh, as the starting point for the salvation of mankind and for each and every believer after their death and until the definitive Resurrection.

The central idea is represented by a great ray of light and the dove of the Holy Spirit which descend from a 'gloria' of musician angels. Next to Our Lady is her sewing basket, with which she has been preparing the Veil of the Temple of Jerusalem, as well as the Burning Bush that appeared to Moses on Mount Tabor. According to the Blessed Alonso de Orozco and other spiritual writers in the 16th century, the Burning Bush became miraculously visible to Mary at the moment of the Conception as an analogous manifestation of God the Father, who is anthropomorphically 'unportrayable'.

This symbolic element may be due to the Augustinian's interest in holding to certain characteristics of the meditations of the Blessed Alonso de Orozco. However, there is a precedent for this subject in Titian's *Annunciation* (Venice), which El Greco may have used as a strictly formal source that was not involved in the implications of Orozco's writings as imposed by his clients. Acquired by the Prado in 1868.

THE RESURRECTION OF CHRIST
(Cat. No. 825)

This very elongated canvas, with its semi-circular format at the top, is still the subject of controversy as to its origins and context. Some experts believe it went with the *Pentecost* as part of the main altarpiece of the Augustinian College of Doña María de Aragón in Madrid, but this hypothesis is not universally accepted. A *Resurrection* existed in the Dominican Church of Our Lady of Atocha in Madrid at the beginning of the 18th century, and some critics equate that painting with this one. Nor do the experts agree on the year it was painted, depending upon whether they

believe it to be from the Dominican church, or linked to the previously mentioned *Pentecost,* which some say was painted at about the same time. Others say that the present work was painted a decade before the *Pentecost.* In any case, its dynamic feeling and the twisted, elongated shapes of the sharply foreshortened bodies concur with the representative manner of El Greco's final years. Here, the play of light and colour is used to create form, and replaces the greater sense of definition we find in the works of El Greco's first years in Spain, as for example, in his *Resurrection* (1577-79) in one of the side-altarpieces in the Convent of Santo Domingo el Antiguo in Toledo. This work came from the Museo de la Trinidad in the 19th century.

THE BAPTISM OF CHRIST
(Cat. No. 821)

This is another signed painting from the Augustinian College of Doña María de Aragón in Madrid. It depicts the Baptism of Jesus and, as an allegory, both the institution of the sacrament that erased original sin, and Christ's obedience to God the Father and his humbleness in letting St. John the Baptist

ments. All of the angels are practically identical, as if the same one were being seen from different views. This traditional Biblical scene was a familiar one to El Greco, who had included a "Baptism" in his very early Venetian *Modena Triptych*. On the other hand, what is new in El Greco's work is the presence of an axe next to St. John the Baptist's knee. It is a symbol taken from a sermon by St. John, Christ's precursor, in which he affirms the future destruction of the Jews, who are unworthy of being considered part of the Chosen People. This painting at the Prado and the *Annunciation* (Cat. No. 3888) are both of very clear provenance. They also epitomize El Greco's ability to transform the most traditional of iconographies and to convert them into something visionary by virtue of their profoundly visual nature. This was, no doubt, just what was needed to show a 16th-century viewer the change reality must have undergone in the supernatural presence of the divine in the natural world.

baptize him. This takes place under a 'gloria' presided over by the Eternal Father. Christ himself is attended by a group of angels who hold his gar-

THE APOSTLE SERIES OF ALMADRONES

Both of the *Apostolados* (Apostle series) conserved in Toledo are considered to be original works by El Greco. The one in the Cathedral was apparently sold to the sacristy in 1676 by the widow of Don Diego Maroto, although it was once thought to have come from the collection of Cardinal Bernardo de Sandoval y Rojas. The other series has been in the El Greco Museum of Toledo since the nineteenth century. Other sets of paintings with the same subjects, the so-called 'Henke Apostles' (perhaps from the Madrilenian convent of Las Baronesas), the San Feliz series (originally in the Convent of San Pelayo in Oviedo) or Almadrones series are cause for some discussion.

The Almadrones series was discovered during the Spanish Civil War (1936-1939) in the village of Almadrones in the province of Guadalajara. The series consists of nine canvases with half-length images of Christ the Redeemer and various apostles. These paintings are now separated between the Prado Museum and several American museums. They were supposedly begun by El Greco and finished after his death by his son and their workshop. They are very late works and are quite heavily restored. Even though they are lesser works if compared to the series in Toledo (especially the outstanding example of the El Greco Museum), the Almadrones series is a far more significant achievement than those of Henke or San Feliz. There are also problems in the identification of the saints, who are depicted without inscriptions and do not always follow the same iconography as the other sets.

SAINT JAMES THE GREAT (Cat. No. 2890)

Along with the *Saviour* and two other apostles (*St. Paul* and *St. Thomas* or *St. Philip*) (Cat. Nos. 2889, 2892, 2891), this painting was once part of a complete Apostle series. The other five (*St. John, St. Andrew, St. Luke, St. Matthew,* and *St. Simon*) are now in museums at Fort Worth, Los Angeles, and Indianapolis. It is signed with the lower-case initials of El Greco's first and last names ('δϑ'). Even though most critics agree

23

that the image is that of St. James the Great, some maintain that it is of St. James the Less. It lacks the traditional symbolic attributes of either apostle, be it St. James the Great with his pilgrim's staff or closed book, or St. James the Less with his shepherd's crook or book, which appear in similar paintings by El Greco. In many cases, El Greco preferred ambiguity or versatility to a clear and precise definition of a saint in his various Apostle series. Acquired by the Prado in 1946.

THE SAVIOUR OF THE WORLD
(Cat. No. 2889)

Christ appears here as *Salvator Mundi*. The half-length figure is clothed in a bright red tunic, his right hand is raised in benediction in the Byzantine manner, and his left hand rests lightly on a globe. This image of Christ is similar to the one in the Henke Apostle series but different from the 'Christ the Redeemer' image of the two Toledo series, in the Cathedral and the El Greco Museum. Like the rest of the Almadrones, as well as the Henke and San Feliz series, this half-length image appears to be a simplification of the three-quarter-length fig- ures of the two Toledo 'Apostolados'. Acquired in 1946.

SAINT THOMAS THE APOSTLE OR SAINT PHILIP
(Cat. No. 2891)

This is the third canvas from the Almadrones Apostle series, which includes the previously mentioned *Saviour* and two other saints (Cat. Nos. 2889, 2890, 2892). Like the *St. James* of the series, it was signed with El Greco's initials, in the same manner as the St. Andrew in Los Angeles, the *St. John the Evangelist* in Fort Worth, and the St. Luke in Indianapolis.

Here, the quality is inferior to the other two in the Prado. It is equally difficult to identify the saint depicted because of the total lack of any symbolic attribute. The present work is similar to the "St. Thomas" in Toledo Cathedral which has an architect's square in his hand, or the one in the El Greco Museum which has a lance. Acquired in 1946.

SAINT PAUL
(Cat. No. 2892)

Along with the *Saviour* and the two other apostles mentioned above (Cat. Nos. 2889, 2890, 2891), this painting was once part of the Apostle series of the parish church of Almadrones. St. Paul is depicted here with the attributes of the sword with which he was beheaded in Rome and a parchment on which is written the beginning of his Letter to Titus, the first bishop of Crete. El Greco often used the figure of St. Paul to emphasize the importance of his island's conversion to Christianity. Of the four paintings in this series on display in the Prado, this one is of the least quality. Acquired by the Prado in 1946.

Saint Jerome as Penitent

This painting depicts the Doctor of the Western Church and translator of the Bible, St. Jerome, as a penitent. The iconography is characteristic of the Counter-Reformation, insisting repeatedly on the validity of the sacrament of penitence, which was questioned by Protestants. El Greco painted St. Jerome several times as a cardinal and with the symbols of his erudition but the image of the saint as a penitent is not altogether unusual in his work, either. The learned St. Jerome, shown naked from the waist up, is beating his chest with a stone while meditating before a crucifix. A cardinal's hat rests behind his back, and he is surrounded by the symbols of the fleeting, transitory nature of earthly life and the inexorable certainty of death, the hourglass and the skull. The instruments of his intellectual work are kept to one side. This is a controversial painting, since some experts consider it authentic. Others, finding no signature, understand that it is from El Greco's workshop and to be dated at the beginning of the 17th century. Some even maintain that it was painted by his Italian assistant, Francesco Prevoste, who accompanied Domenikos Theotokopoulos to Spain from Rome. It seems to be a replica of an original now hanging in the National Gallery of Scotland in Edinburgh. Its provenance is unknown. On deposit from the Comunidad de Madrid.

The Adoration of the Shepherds
(Cat. No. 2988)

Technique and style help us date this great painting from the last years of El Greco's life in Toledo. It is unsigned, but it is clearly by his own hand. It comes from the Convent of Santo Domingo el Antiguo in Toledo. The work was painted specifically for the altarpiece of the burial chapel which El Greco had built for himself in the nave of the convent church, once he obtained permission to be buried there with his family in 1612. It was there that the canvas was appraised and recorded in 1618, four years after the master's death, by his pupil and fellow painter, Luis Tristán (c. 1586-Toledo, 1624), who said he had actually seen the master paint it. Tristán made his appraisal at the moment in which the Theotocopouli family vault was being moved to the Convent of San Torcuato, also in Toledo. The altarpiece and its gilded frame were left behind in Santo Domingo el Antiguo. El Greco's mortal remains were buried in San Torcuato, but when this church disappeared, all traces of his burial site vanished. It has been said that the painting was once part of a larger altarpiece, still in existence at the church of Santo Domingo el Antiguo, whose architecture was also attributed to El Greco. Today, we know that this later altarpiece belonged to the Sebastián de Huerta family, who were related to the Cardinal-Archbishop of Toledo, Don Bernardo de Sandoval y Rojas. It was made by the

sculptor and architect Alonso Carbonel (1619) and the painters Eugenio Caxés (*Annunciation,* 1620) and Angelo Nardi (*Martyrdom of St. Sebastian* and *The Portiuncula*). El Greco adorned his own funerary painting with a simpler, more modest frame that was more in keeping with his finances and social position. It is still *in situ,* surrounding a Baroque canvas of St. Mary Magdalene dei Pazzi and St. Augustine by an unknown artist. El Greco's *Adoration* is an exceptional work, painted by the artist for himself and his family as a definitive testimony to his religious faith and to his art. Within a cave-like space in a manger, the nocturnal scene depicts the adoration of the shepherds, to whom Mary shows the Child, who is in turn the painting's source of light since he is understood to be the *Lux Mundi.* Overhead, a 'gloria' of angels show a scroll bearing the inscription *Gloria in excelsis...* The greatly elongated figures are full of movement and emerge from the darkness by means of strong backlighting and complicated postures. In contrast, the vivid colour and the flesh tones are remarkably intense despite El Greco's use of a cool palette. The sombre mood of this painting has been attributed to the influence of Roman Caravaggism, which came to El Greco after his pupil Luis Tristán returned from a study tour to Italy. Nevertheless, it may also be the result of El Greco's having adjusted the subject matter of the painting to its worldly circumstances which called for a nocturnal setting for the adoration of the shepherds. We should also stress the dramatic effect created by the descent of divine and angelic light upon the manger of Bethlehem. This, in turn, emphasizes the intervention of the miraculous and the supernatural upon the traditional medium of natural and visible reality. Acquired in 1954.

Saint John the Evangelist
(Cat. No. 2444)

Although its provenance is unknown and it lacks a signature, this painting is generally accepted by experts as authentic because of its high quality. The Evangelist is shown more than half-length, and he holds the unmistakable chalice — a symbol of his having remained miraculously unharmed after drinking a poison — in his right hand. He wears a green tunic and a crimson mantle. The painting can be dated around 1600. Even though the pose is the same as in other images of the Saint of Patmos in El Greco's Apostle series, critics do not believe this to be part of yet another series. Rather, they tend to think it was an independent devotional image which might originally have been full-length. It may have come from an altarpiece, on account of St. John's looking off to our right and using his left hand to show his symbol. There is another painting of the saint facing the other way, also a three-quarter-length image, at Scripps College in Claremont, California. But experts fail to agree on the authenticity of this second canvas; some make the rather unlikely claim that it is a copy from a lost engraving by the Flemish artist from Malines, Diego de Astor, who was active in Toledo making engravings of El Greco's works. Donated by Dr. César Cabañas in 1921.

**The Holy Face
(Veronica's Veil)**
(Cat. No. 2874)

This canvas is closely related to the oval *Holy Face* of the main altarpiece of Santo Domingo el Antiguo in Toledo. Even so, the treatment is less naturalistic, and its horizontal format more closely resembles El Greco's more narrative paintings on the theme of St. Veronica. As in all of these works, the image of the face of Christ does not merge with the folds of the cloth. The 'holy image' remains intact, without deformities. Yet, the icon-like quality does not lose any of the naturalistic possibilities of optical illusion which allow the face to follow the undulating movements of its physical support. Despite its lack of a signature and its heavily restored condition, most experts accept this work as authentic. It is thought to be a later version, painted in the late 1590's, of an earlier painting (now in a private collection in New York) which is signed with capital initials in the manner of El Greco's Italian years. The present work is stylistically linked to a *Veronica* which was also originally the property of the Convent of Santo Domingo el Antiguo, but later belonged to the art historian María Luisa Caturla and today is part of a private collection. Acquired in 1944 with funds from the legacy of the Count of Cartagena, from the parish church of Móstoles in the Madrid region, where it had hung in the sacristy.

Christ Bearing the Cross
(Cat. No. 822)

This painting probably came from the now-disappeared Carmelite monastery of San Hermenegildo in Madrid, where it was listed in the inventories of the 18th century. It is signed with small letters, the last syllables of which are hard to make out. It can be dated in the last decade of the 16th century. It shows a more than half-length figure of Christ bearing the Cross on the road to Calvary. It is one of many existing versions of the same theme, which is an iconic reduction of this episode of the Passion. Some of the other versions are also to be found in Spain, in the Treasury of the Cathedral of Cuenca, in the parish churches of Santa Catalina in El Bonillo (Albacete) and San Esteban in Olot (Gerona), and in the National Art Museum of Catalonia in Barcelona. As often happens with El Greco's other compositions, the various versions reveal the success he had with these smaller paintings in Madrid and Toledo. They were undoubtedly acquired as devotional images by private individuals. This would explain the fact that Christ is seen from below, and without any visual connection between his image and the viewer. However, this painting breaks with the tradition of such Passion images: El Greco does not insist upon Christ's physical suffering. Rather, he seems to stress the dignity, the stylized beauty, and the divine nature of the God-Man, whose gaze seems locked in silent dialogue with an invisible God the Father more than on a virtual Calvary. The painting arrived at the Prado in 1877 from the Museo de la Trinidad.

33

The Coronation of the Virgin
(Cat. No. 2645)

Signed in lower-case letters and dated to the early 1590's, this painting of the coronation of the Virgin Mary seems to be the first version that El Greco made of the subject. The Virgin is seated above a crescent moon, which introduces the idea of her Immaculate Conception. She is crowned by God the Father and God the Son, with the dove that is symbolic of the Holy Spirit between two groups of minute cherubim at the apex of the rhombus that divides the composition. The image was no doubt inspired by a print by the German Renaissance artist Albrecht Dürer. In the background, as in other versions of this subject, there is an angel kneeling almost with his back to the viewer so as to point towards the Holy Spirit. The whole composition is organized as if suspended in the air and as though the central image were meant to be contemplated from below. Unlike the later versions of the subject, from the upper section of the altarpiece from Talavera la Vieja (Cáceres) (now in the Monastery of Our Lady of Guadalupe) and from the main altar of the Chapel of San José in Toledo, here the scene does not include a group of saints. The present painting is much closer to an even later image at the Hospital de la Caridad in Illescas (Toledo), despite the oval shape of that canvas. The Illescas painting — a *quadro riportato* — originally adorned the centre of the vaulted ceiling over the church's high altar.

The Virgin Mary
(Cat. No. 829)

Signed in lower-case Greek letters (although with a few suspicious mistakes) and datable to around 1600, this bust-length image shows an almost frontal view of Mary, wrapped in a red tunic and with her head covered with a white wimple under a blue mantle. A luminous halo surrounds her head and stresses its volume against a dark neutral background, making use of unconventional means to emphasize her sacred nature. She turns her eyes directly towards the viewer, which underscores her nearness and her psychological involvement with anyone who approaches this image in devotion. It seems to be the only existing replica (authentic according to most historians) of the original at the Musée des Beaux-Arts in Strasbourg which is also signed but with the correct spelling of the painter's surname. The Strasbourg painting is from the same period and of slightly better quality. Just as we see to a lesser extent with the subject of 'Mary, Mother of Sorrows', this fact reveals the limited success that El Greco had with paintings of the Virgin as a unique object of pious meditation. This is perhaps an indirect reflection of the devotional interests of the Castilians in the time of Philip II, or El Greco's relative uneasiness with painting this type of isolated, grief-stricken and aging female figures in whom he could not accentuate physical beauty.

Saint Antony of Padua
(Cat. No. 815)

This painting was signed XEIR DOMENIKOU, in the way El Greco used during his early years in Spain. Although its provenance is unsure until its arrival at the Museo de la Trinidad after the disentailment of the monasteries in the 19th century, El Greco's signature seems to set the date at between 1577 and 1579. Some critics (without doubting its authenticity) would date it towards the last decade of the century. We see a more than half-length figure holding a lily in his right hand and a small image of the Christ Child in his left. This runs counter to the traditional symbolism of the saint since it is more usual to portray Christ as a flesh-and-blood child instead of through an image. This depiction of the Franciscan saint — the only one known of by El Greco — lacks some of the strength of his more characteristic paintings, perhaps because of its overall darkening with age and poor state of preservation, which have affected the colour. A recent X-ray study has shown that the image of the Christ Child is the result of later repainting, to adapt El Greco's painting to a more habitual iconography of St. Antony. No other version of this Franciscan theme is known to exist. It comes from the Museo de la Trinidad.

Saint Paul
(Cat. No. 814)

This almost half-length image shows St. Paul holding a large closed book in his hands. He is wearing a blue tunic and a red mantle. The painting itself lacks a signature, but was recorded in the Alcázar of Madrid in 1686 and 1694. After this royal residence burned to the ground in 1734, the painting was moved to the Buen Retiro Palace. Because the saint depicted here has none of the unmistakable symbols of an apostle, it has sometimes been identified as St. Bartholomew instead. According to one theory, it was one of the paintings that remained in El Greco's Toledo workshop and was listed there in an inventory after his death. Be that as it may, the bearded figure more closely resembles depictions of St. Matthew in the Apostle series at the Cathedral and the El Greco Museum in Toledo, or in the Almadrones series (Indianapolis), or even the St. Matthew (or St. Philip, as its inscription apparently mistakenly reads) of the San Feliz series. Logically, this painting is linked with the sets of apostles that El Greco undertook so often that his workshop practically became an assembly line. This one, however, is of far better quality than the Almadrones painting at the Prado Museum. Stylistic evidence suggests that it was probably painted around 1600; some scholars have even doubted its authenticity, thinking it more likely a product of El Greco's workshop.

Saint Andrew and Saint Francis
(Cat. No. 2819)

Painted in the late 1590's and signed in lower-case letters, this canvas comes from the Convent of the Incarnation in Madrid. It was not one of the original works commissioned when the convent was founded. Rather, it was donated in 1676 by Sister Ana Agustina del Niño Jesús, a daughter of the Duke of Abrantes, as a personal contribution to the convent. St. Andrew bearing his cross, and a hooded St. Francis with his friar's habit and the stigmata, both highly stylized full-length figures, engage in lively conversation against a landscape-filled background. We see the figures from a very low viewpoint. The composition of the saints' bodies and the gestures of their hands are superbly elegant: St. Andrew's right hand is outstretched as if arguing a point, while St. Francis's left hand rests delicately on his chest in a gesture of faithful meditation. The large cross becomes a nexus for the unity of the composition as well as the colour between the two saints. The contrasting colours of their garments (green and blue for St. Andrew, and dark grey for St. Francis) go well together thanks to the hues of the background sky and landscape that frame them and reflect them. This painting seems to be a fusion, perhaps at the client's request, of El Greco's full-length figures of St. Andrew (as the one at the Metropolitan Museum in New York) and the innumerable three-quarter-length depictions of St. Francis. This procedure was used in pairing other saints with St. Francis in several other paintings as well. Acquired from the Convent of the Incarnation in 1942.

The Annunciation (Cat. No. 827)

This unsigned painting in tempera on wooden panel is the only work from El Greco's Italian period at the Prado Museum. It was probably done in Venice around 1570, shortly after the artist set himself up in Rome. Nevertheless, its small

size has led many to suspect, as so often happens in other cases, that it was a preliminary study for a larger painting rather than a finished work in its own right. This was not uncommon for El Greco to do, according the testimony of the painter and writer Francisco Pacheco (who was also to be Diego Velázquez's master and father-in-law) after he visited El Greco's Toledo workshop in 1611. It seems more likely that this is a completely independent work. The use of wooden panel and tempera is justified when we consider that the late Byzantine tradition of painting in which El Greco was first trained and took so long to abandon for canvas and oil. The composition seems based on that of a lost work by Titian but known through an engraving by Gian Giacomo Caraglio that El Greco had already used for one or his earliest Venetian paintings, the "Annunciation" of the *Modena Triptych*. Using this graphic source as a guide, El Greco added background architec- ture with a street in radical perspective. He also followed the models of urban perspective published by Sebastiano Serlio in his treatise on architecture. Nevertheless, El Greco's handling of multi-viewpoint perspective, situated on a vertical axis, betrays his still-precarious grasp of an otherwise characteristic Renaissance method. It was something that seemed to obsess him during his Italian years, as he sought to add spatial depth to his paintings by turning to chessboard-like paving stones, which became tremendously complicated as different levels of pavement were introduced. Despite its technique, this work is entirely Venetian in terms of its composition, colour, light, space, and brushwork, all of which El Greco was trying to assimilate. On the other hand, the proportional relationship of the figures to their surrounding context seems to show the influence of Roman art. Acquired in 1868.

Saint Sebastian
(Cat. Nos. 3002, 7186)

Countess of Mora. Despite its oval shape, which is probably due to having been cut down at a later date, this painting resembles a slightly earlier, more refined but more poorly conserved *St. Sebastian* that hung in the Royal Palace of Bucharest (now in a private collection). Much more, in fact, than the imposing image of this saint in the Cathedral of Palencia. The Palencia version was painted shortly after El Greco's arrival in Toledo and depicts the saint in a more heroic manner, a more mature figure painted with greater attention to the anatomy of the nude. At some point in the past, the Prado Museum's canvas was cut off in the lower half. The fragment shows the martyred saint's legs against the background of the banks of the Tagus River from a very low viewpoint, in El Greco's customary manner. The lower part was acquired by the Prado Museum in 1987 from an unidentified private collection in Madrid. The upper section was donated in 1959 by the Marchioness of Casa Riera and Dowager Countess of Mora, in memory of the Marquess of Casa Torres.

A greater than half-length figure seen from a very low viewpoint, St. Sebastian is depicted at the moment of his martyrdom. He turns his head toward heaven as the arrows strike him. The painting is considered to be a very late work in El Greco's career, from around 1605. Part of the image may have been painted by his workshop, although not all experts agree with this hypothesis. It is unsigned, and its original owners are unknown. More recently, it belonged to the Marchioness of Casa Riera and

Allegory
(Cat. No. 7657)

Recently acquired with funds from the Villaescusa legacy (1993), this scene has been identified with a painting from the Valencian collection of the Colegio del Patriarca Juan de Ribera (1611), or with an *Allegory* or one of the two versions of the *Boy Lighting a Candle* listed in the inventory of Jorge Manuel Theotocopouli's paintings in his workshop in 1621. It is the Prado Museum's only non-religious work by El Greco, aside from his portraits. Its date is hard to ascertain, though it must be a later work, from the early 1600's. It is also difficult to clarify the meaning of the image: a monkey, a boy lighting a candle, and a slow-witted man. It may be a recreation or a modernized *ekphrasis* of a long-lost image by the painter Antiphilus or the sculptor Buthieus from antiquity. El Greco may have wanted to try his hand at competing with them in a colouristic depiction of fire in the Venetian style of Jacopo Bassano. This *Allegory*, of which two other versions are known to exist (Harewood Collection, London, and National Gallery of Scotland, Edinburgh), has been related to the Spanish saying "Man is fire, woman is tow, and the Devil blows them into a flame", to suggest a moralizing intention and criticism of erotic passion. It might also be possible to interpret it as a combination of ideas: an improvement on painting from antiquity, and a humorous look at the limited possibilities of imitation, from the ape, who seems to want to blow in the manner of a 'dauber', to the half-wit, who is content just with admiring the phenomenon.

This genre was scarcely cultivated by Spanish artists in the 16th century. Charles V turned more often than not to the Venetian artist Titian, and Philip II to the Dutch painter Antonio Moro or the Italian artist Sofinisba Anguisciola, before employing Alonso Sánchez Coello and Juan Pantoja de la Cruz. But El Greco stood out both in Italy *(Giorgio Giulio Clovio, Vicenzo Anastagi)* and in Spain, even though he never managed to receive a commission from the royal family or the upper nobility of Castile. The royal portrait was kept alive under Philip II by Sánchez Coello and Pantoja, who followed Netherlandish models (distant, accurate, detailed in description and highly representational). El Greco, on the other hand, developed another kind of portraiture which was freer in the handling of form, and direct and lively in the physical depiction of his models, which are full of movement and immediate vitality. He was also penetrating in his psychological treatment. The artist deviated considerably from the archetypes of the stately portrait, almost always painted against a neutral background. These characteristics only got stronger over the years, leading to masterpieces such as *Francisco de Pisa* and *Fray Hortensio Félix Paravicino*. It comes as no surprise that this is where he achieved his first successes in Rome in the early 1570's. He continued to use it as he delved into his own image. He was one of the first Spanish painters to cultivate the self-portrait, whether as an independent piece or inserted into other genres such as religious ones. Let us not forget that, time and time again, he put portraits of well-known contemporaries into his religious paintings, perhaps with the íntention of bringing religious events closer to the immediate world. This Venetian practice brought him grief when he was sued by some of his clients, such as the Brotherhood of the Hospital of Our Lady of Charity in Illescas who were shocked to find El Greco's son among the faithful surrounding the figure of the Virgin. El Greco also made a privileged place for himself in the history of painting in this genre. He was able to reap greater satisfactions here in his own lifetime than with his much more censured religious paintings. After his death, he won the steady acclaim of critics who often identified the extravagances of his religious images with physical or mental disorders yet fully accepted his lucidity when looking at his portraits.

His principal clients in this genre were magistrates, members of the lesser nobility of Toledo, or from time to time a high dignitary of the Church (for example, the Cardinal-Inquisitor Fernando Niño de Guevara), a politician such as Don Rodrigo Vázquez de Arce, or a lady. They seem to have come from his own immediate circle; many were friends. El Greco ran counter to the norms of the moment by depicting them full of life. Though his portraits never met with any success in the more formal context of Philip II's court, paintings such as the *Burial of the Lord of Orgaz* elicited great admiration among viewers as early as the 1580's. Many of the people he portrayed can be traced to the painters of Toledo in the early 1600's, from Luis Tristán to Fray Juan Bautista Maino. This sometimes gives rise to confusion among historians with respect to his work in this genre.

It is not surprising, then, that El Greco's example was taken up decades later, well after his death, by Diego Velázquez, who proclaimed his admiration for El Greco's Toledan pupil, Luis Tristán, and even kept some of El Greco's portraits as models in his studio in the Royal Alcázar of Madrid.

The Doctor and Poet Don Rodrigo de la Fuente
(Cat. No. 807)

This portrait bearing a signature in lower-case Greek letters was hanging in the 'Galería del Cierzo' of the Royal Alcázar of Madrid in 1686. It was moved to the Buen Retiro Palace after the fire in the Alcázar of Christmas 1734 which razed the traditional royal seat of the Spanish Habsburgs. It has sometimes been identified as the physician Luis

de Mercado (the ring on the thumb of his left hand would indicate his doctoral degree) but it more likely portrays another physician, Rodrigo de la Fuente, who was cited by Miguel de Cervantes in *La ilustre fregona*. He was also the father of Ruy Pérez de la Fuente, who was chaplain and priest at the parish of Santo Tomé in Toledo, and one of the personages identified in the group in the *Burial of the Lord of Orgaz*. Evidence for identifying him as Rodrigo (his son has also been suggested) comes from its resemblance to a portrait bearing his name in the Biblioteca Nacional of Madrid. This personage, apparently a personal friend of the painter's, was a descendant of Toledan Jews that had converted to Christianity. He was a professor at the University of Santa Catalina in Toledo. He died in 1589, which may determine the time of this painting. The left hand of this half-length figure rests on an open book on a table (unlike texts and writings in other works by El Greco, this book has not been identified). His right hand — quite retouched at present — is held in a position of calm discussion, full of life and superb immediacy.

Gentleman with Hand on Chest
(Cat. No. 809)

This painting, signed in capital letters, is perhaps the most famous and representative of the portraits El Greco made of Toledan nobility. It came from the so-called 'Quinta' of the Duke of El Arco where it was recorded in 1794. The gentleman portrayed is still unknown. Attempts have been made to identify him as the Marquess of Montemayor, Juan de Silva, who was a knight of the Order of Santiago and chief notary of Toledo. Because of his posture and the presence of a sword and a pendant, the painting is thought to commemorate his taking an oath of office. Restoration of the canvas has revealed a grossly deformed shoulder, which seems to confirm the identification since Juan de Silva is known to have been incapacitated by a harquebus-shot wound in the Battle of Alcázarquivir in 1578. Stylistically, it resembles other works from El Greco's early years in Toledo, which would make it one of the first portraits he painted in Spain. The sitter's static and rigid posture, and the almost completely full-face view give the portrait a ritual and hieratic air that is emphasized by

the orthogonal directions of the lighted areas. The vertical lines of the face and the sword intersect with the horizontal lines of the elegantly open hand on the chest (the middle and ring fingers together, however, in true Italian Renaissance fashion). They stand out against the black clothing and the neutral grey of the background that appeared after the restoration (replacing the black background of before). The subject's withdrawn dignity is accentuated by the lack of connection with the viewer. He looks self-absorbed, without any visual relationship with us. He shows us his physical features but withholds his individual personality.

Don Rodrigo Vázquez de Arce
(Cat. No. 808)

Identified by an inscription, Rodrigo Vázquez de Arce was born in Avila around 1529 and died in 1599. He was Keeper of the Keys in the Order of Alcantara, judge of the famous royal secretary Antonio Pérez and executor of the will of Don Gaspar Quiroga, archbishop of Toledo. He also presided over the Royal Council of Castile, the governing body that commissioned El Greco to do the main altarpiece for the Madrilenian College of Doña María de Aragón in 1596. This may have been the motive for commissioning this portrait, or

the original this version is based on, as well as the one at the Pushkin Museum in Moscow. Furthermore, records show the existence of several versions in various collections in Madrid in the 17th century. Two of them belonged to the collection of Agustín de Hierro, a fellow Council member, who owned a very rich selection of El Greco's works. Like other portraits at the Prado, it came to the museum from the Royal Alcázar of Madrid, where it had been inventoried, passing later to the 'Quinta' of the Duke of El Arco. Experts are hesitant to consider it an authentic work, painted shortly before Don Rodrigo's fall into disgrace and his death. Neither do they agree as to whether it is a copy of a lost original, since so many unsigned versions of this work appeared in the inventories of Madrilenian collections in the 1600's, and because the brushwork is rather stiff.

A Gentleman
(Cat. No 806)

This bust-length portrait is signed in cursive letters and has been identified with a portrait listed in the inventories of 1666, 1686 and 1700 in the Royal Alcázar of Madrid where it hung near the entrance to the 'Galería del Cierzo'.

We see little more than the head, almost as if it had been cut down from a larger portrait. The sitter is an anonymous grey-haired but youthful gentleman whose kindly face is turned slightly in a three-quarter view. Experts have not yet succeeded in determining the man's identity. But from the kind of ruff collar he wears, we can make him out to be a Toledan *hidalgo* under the reign of Philip II. Historians have dated the canvas to some time between 1580 and 1600 without being able to ascertain its exact year. On the other hand, all of them agree on its outstanding quality. Stylistically, it shows a prodigious diversity of textures and flesh tones, from the passages in which the impasto is so thin that we can see the bluish grey base and even the weave of the canvas, to other areas with rich impasto, as in the treatment of the sitter's short ruff collar. This portrait also stands out for the expressiveness of his sensitive face and for his clear and good-natured, rather than penetrating, gaze. All of this brings the viewer closer to the model despite his self-absorption. It is beyond a doubt one of the most attractive portraits El Greco ever painted.

**Don Julián Romero
de las Hazañas and his
patron saint, St. Julian**
(Cat. No. 2445)

An inscription on this portrait identifies the subject as the Knight Commander of the Order of Santiago, Julián Romero, called 'el de las Hazañas' or 'of the great feats'. He was born in Antequera in the province of Malaga, and became a famous military field-master on the battlefields of Flanders and Italy. He was admitted to the Order of Santiago in 1558, and died near the Italian town of Cremona in 1578. This whole legend may be apocryphal, since it has been discovered that he was in fact born in Huélamo or Torrejoncillo de Huete in the province of Cuenca in 1518.

In either case, this is a posthumous portrait that may have been paired with another painting of a strictly religious nature. Julián Romero would then be kneeling before a sacred figure in an attitude of worship, presented by his patron saint. This latter is St. Julian, wearing contemporary armour, a blue mantle with fleurs-de-lis, a plumed helmet, and a ducal coronet. Some experts have suggested that the saintly figure may actually be St. Louis of France, or even St. Theodore.

Critics also suggest the date of the painting to be in the late 1590's, but they differ as to how much of it was done by El Greco's workshop. This funerary portrait, which contains such traditional elements as the column, apparently came from Alcalá la Real in the province of Jaen, where it remained in the hands of the gentleman's descendants until 1890. This is the only portrait of its kind by El Greco. From the bequest of Don Luis de Errazu in 1926.

Young Gentleman
(Cat. No. 811)

Signed in lower-case Greek letters, this painting came from the Duke of El Arco's collection. It can be dated to the first years of the 1600's. The sitter for this bust-length portrait of a man in a black coat and a large ruff collar who is seen in a three-quarter view is still unidentified. Some attempts have been made to link it to the Toledan poet Baltasar Elisio de Medinilla (1585-1620), who was secretary to the first Count of Mora, Don Francisco de Rojas y Guzmán, head of one of the most famous academies or 'tertulias' in Toledo at the time. Noblemen, intellectuals and poets, such as the unfortunate Medinilla himself, met at this academy. Medinilla was killed by the Lord of Olias, Don Jerónimo de Andrada y Rivadeneira, in an ambush. The name of Eugenio Manzanas, another of the poets in this circle, has also been associated with some of El Greco's portraits. If the identification with Baltasar Elisio is correct, it would be the only known portrait of this follower of the lyrical poetry of the famous playwright Lope de Vega, author of several poems a lo divino and one narrative poem, "Description of Buenavista", the Toledan township of Cardinal Don Bernardo de Sandoval y Rojas where another literary academy met in the early 17th century. The quality of this portrait is excellent, which has helped experts to agree on its authenticity. It is an admirable psychological portrait of a gentleman who, from the style of his attire, rived in the reign of Philip III.

A Gentleman
(Cat. No. 810)

This bust-length portrait is of a gentleman with dark hair and salt-and-pepper beard who is dressed in a black cape and an enormous ruff collar. It also comes from the 'Quinta' of the Duke of El Arco, where it was hanging at the end of the 18th century. Signed in lower-case Greek letters, it is a painting of very high quality, dating from the beginning of the 17th century. The man portrayed has not been identified, but judging by his large collar, this voluminous gentleman of imposing personality must have been an *hidalgo* during the reign of Philip III. A few scholars have put forth some rather shaky arguments connecting this likeness to the writer Miguel de Cervantes Saavedra, the future author of *Don Quixote de la Mancha*. At the time this work was painted — the exact year is still elusive — Cervantes was recognized only as a poet. He did spend a lengthy period of time in Esquivias, a township near the Imperial City of Toledo, in 1604. He surely went up to the city at this time. He was a friend of the parish priest of Santo Tomé, Andrés Núñez de Madrid, who was also a client and acquaintance (if not a friend) of the painter.

Despite the unjustified identification of this image with Spain's greatest writer, its provenance from the Duke of El Arco's collection may allow us to link it to one of Toledo's learned men who frequented the academies that met at villas and 'cigarrales'. In most cases, we have no idea what they looked like individually.

Trinitarian or Dominican Friar
(Cat. No. 2644)

This small bust-length portrait's lack of a signature has allowed some experts to think it was a preliminary study for a larger painting. In any case, it is considered to be absolutely authentic, and from El Greco's final years. It shows a friar of the Trinitarian order. Years ago, it was identified as a portrait of the Dominican friar and painter, Fray Juan Bautista Maino (Pastrana, Guadalajara, 1581-Madrid, 1649), who was active in Toledo during the decade between 1601 and 1611, and joined the Order of Preachers in 1613. Since El Greco died the following year, these dates exclude such an identification. Even so, the face does resemble the supposed self-portrait of Maino as a page pointing to the scene of the Epiphany in one of the canvases of the altarpiece at his convent of San Pedro Mártir in Toledo. We know two of El Greco's close ties with the Trinitarians of Madrid and Toledo. One was his personal friend-ship with the 'conceptist' poet Fray Hortensio Félix de Paravicino y Arteaga (1580-1633), whose portrait he painted in 1609 (Museum of Fine Arts, Boston, and a copy with variations in a private collection in Madrid). The other was the portrait he did at his own initiative of Paravicino's fellow friar and mentor, the future saint, Fray Juan Bautista de la Concepción (1561-1613) while he was living in Toledo between 1610 and 1612; El Greco was amazed at the striking contrast between his exhuberant physique and his ascetic face. A legacy to the Prado from Don Pablo Bosch.

A Gentleman
(Cat. No. 813)

Unsigned, of relatively mechanical execution, and in less-than-perfect condition, this portrait comes from the Duke of El Arco's collection (where it was recorded in 1794). This, once again, leads to the likelihood that it depicts someone from the intellectual circles of Toledo towards the end of the 16th century. It remains completely anonymous, as no identification has yet been offered. It is a portrait of a middle-aged gentleman with large ears, dark hair, a moustache and goatee, and a slightly impertinent expression. It has been dated to the 1580's, when El Greco began to accentuate the three-dimensionality of his religious and portrait paintings, although some critics propose a later date. Against a very dark neutral background, the elongated bust is shown with the torso in a three-quarter view, emphasizing only the face and the white ruff collar of an anonymous gentleman of the time of Philip II. He looks at us very directly, but without revealing an even minimally interesting personality. It is perhaps one of El Greco's least attractive portraits, not only at the Prado, but in his whole Spanish oeuvre. Experts agree that it is authentic, nonetheless.

The Jurist Don Jerónimo de Cevallos (Cat. No. 812)

Thanks to an engraved portrait made in 1613 by the Toledan artist Pedro Ángel, as well as other canvases of the period, this portrait has been identified as that of Cevallos, a famous jurist in Toledo and, after 1626, a priest at the Cathedral there. He was born into a noble family in Escalona in 1562 and died in 1641. He studied at Salamanca and Valladolid, taught in Avila and Salamanca, was a city councillor in Toledo, and an assiduous member of the Count of Mora's academy, although he basically wrote only learned works on his speciality, jurisprudence. He did write a few laudatory verses as a prologue for his friend Baltasar Elisio de Medinilla's poem "Limpia Concepción de Nuestra Señora". Like other portraits by El Greco in the Prado Museum, it comes from the 'Quinta' of the Duke of El Arco. This certain identification of the sitter has given cause for the supposition that other male portraits from the same estate were part of a series of images of the members of this literary academy or 'tertulia'. The Dominican friar and painter Fray Juan Bautista Maino painted just such a gallery of portraits for this group. El Greco himself seems to have frequented the academy of the Count of Fuensalida, at least before 1609. Although it is not signed, this portrait is unanimously considered to be one of the best from El Greco's final years (Cevallos did not arrive in Toledo until 1600 and a document records the painting exactly in 1608). Its free and open brushwork, and the incredible physical and psychological immediacy of the sitter make it remarkable. Cevallos has also been identified as the gentleman portrayed by Fray Juan Bautista Maino (Prado Cat. No. 2595).

THE SON: JORGE MANUEL THEOTOCÓPULI
(1578-1613)

El Greco's son was born in Toledo in 1578. His mother, Jerónima de las Cuevas, who was apparently of plebeian origins, seems to have disappeared very early on. Jorge Manuel was educated in his father's workshop from the time he was a young boy. We know his face as a child thanks to the *Burial of the Lord of Orgaz* in Santo Tomé in Toledo. We see him as a young man in the painting of *Our Lady of Charity* in the Hospital of Illescas, and once again, in the portrait that El Greco made of his son as a painter (Seville, Museo de Bellas Artes). Although he favoured architecture as a profession, Jorge Manuel excelled more at rendering his imaginative structures in drawings than he did at actually building them. Even so, he was eventually named 'master architect' at the Cathedral of Toledo. From the beginning of the 17th century, Jorge Manuel worked in his father's workshop doing altarpieces and paintings; at other times, he worked independently, carrying out such works as the altarpiece of Titulcia (now Bayona de Tajuña, 1607-1621). When his father died in 1614, he continued the activities of El Greco's workshop. He followed his father's style in painting, often re-using the small models or 'studies' on panel that El Greco had made when preparing for a large painting or creating new compositions. But the quality of his work suffered the consequences of being only a series of remakes, as they gradually became stereotypes of the commonplace. He also took on the work of designing and building altarpieces such as the one for Santa Clara la Real (1623), which would include paintings by Luis Tristán. Jorge Manuel was married three times, and he was always hounded by economic problems. This eventually led to the seizure of his property and to the subsequent poverty of his family. He died in Toledo on March 29, 1631.

Expolio (Disrobing of Christ)
(Cat. No. 832)

This small painting dates to the late 1590's and is signed by "J. Manuel Theotocópuli". It is a copy of El Greco's *Expolio* or *Disrobing of Christ* that was painted between 1577 and 1579 for the sacristy of the Cathedral of Toledo as one of the first works he executed in the Imperial City. It may also be a copy of the version of the *Expolio* done for the parish church of Santa Leocadia (now in the Museo de Santa Cruz of Toledo). Jorge Manuel's canvas clearly shows the process of artistic deterioration to which some of the father's masterpieces were subjected by his son. While keeping the original composition practically intact, Jorge Manuel has made the forms harder by accentuating the contours of the figures and losing the subtleties of shading, colour, play of light, brilliance, and reflections.

The figures have lost their former consistency, becoming excessively sentimental or overly schematic almost to the point of caricature. The dignity and the sense of majesty we find in El Greco's original is missing, especially in the figure of Christ at the humiliating moment of being stripped of his garments by the throng of hangmen and soldiers. Worth noting is the presence of the Three Maries in the foreground. The Gospels make no mention of their being there; hence, the Cathedral Chapter found a motive for filing the first of a long series of lawsuits against El Greco during his years in Toledo. On the other hand, the Crown of Thorns does appear on Christ's head.

THE PUPIL: LUIS TRISTÁN

Luis de Escamilla or Luis Tristán, as he signed his paintings, was born in a village of the province of Toledo. He joined El Greco's workshop in 1603. At the end of this decade, he went to Italy (Venice, Florence, and Rome) and left us some of the impressions of his trip in notes he made in the copy of Giorgio Vasari's *Lives* that had previously belonged to El Greco. In Italy, Tristán came into contact with the colourist tendencies of Venice and with Roman naturalism, which was based primarily on the art of Michelangelo Merisi da Caravaggio. In 1611, perhaps after a short stay in Seville, Tristán was back in Toledo. From that time on he worked as an independent painter. He remained on close terms with his former master and with El Greco's son, Jorge Manuel, who was his almost exact contemporary.

Tristán's most important works were always highly individualized. The two best examples are the altarpieces at Yepes, in the province of Toledo (1616) and Santa Clara in Toledo (1621-1624). But despite his death at an early age, he also left a significant number of religious images and portraits. His style is a very personal one that combines the underlying influence of El Greco (models, compositions, colour) with his own interpretation of Italian Caravaggism and a clearer and more classicistic version of the work of Fray Juan Bautista Maino. We may also detect the influence of the innovations of Annibale Carracci and Guido Reni, as well as the naturalism of Pedro Orrente (Murcia, c. 1580-Valencia, 1645). Along with Maino and Orrente, who worked only sporadically in Toledo, Tristán became the third basic figure of the Toledo school of painting during the early decades of the 17th century.

Unknown Old Man (Cat. No. 1158)

This is a less-than-half-length portrait of a gentleman with a grey beard, dressed in black with a ruff collar of the style that was fashionable in the reign of Philip II. A restoration of the painting covered up the sitter's right hand, which apparently was holding a rod. The painting follows the lines of El Greco's later period, in its immediate and intense depiction of the model and in the strong individuality that makes direct contact with the viewer. However, the facial details are more minutely described and more sculptural than they are in El Greco's portraits. Thus it differs from the type of portrait that was being done in Toledo at that moment by younger artists such as Blas de Prado (Camarena, Toledo, c. 1545-Madrid, 1599) or Antón Pizarro (Toledo, active 1594-Toledo, 1622). Unfortunately, the man portrayed here has never been identified. The painting comes from the Royal Alcázar of Madrid, where it hung in the 18th century and was considered to be from the school of El Greco, even though it was attributed for some time to the Italian painter Antonio Stella. Its thick brushwork in the Venetian manner, which is similar to the one he used for the Yepes altarpiece, has helped to maintain the attribution of this portrait to Luis Tristán.

Other paintings by El Greco outside the Prado Museum

The Prado Museum houses the world's most important collection of El Greco's paintings, even if the Imperial City of Toledo — where he lived from 1577 to 1614 — does have a larger total number of them (Cathedral, Museo de Santa Cruz, El Greco Museum, Convent of Santo Domingo el Antiguo, Chapel of San José, Santo Tomé parish church, Hospital de Tavera, etc.). The paintings in the Prado's collection came from several sources. Some are from the royal collections, donated by Ferdinand VII. Others came from the former Museo de la Trinidad, which brought together many works from the monasteries and convents that were suppressed during the Disentailment of the 19th century. Together they provide a very complete panorama of the Cretan painter's Spanish work in the two genres that he cultivated most: religious images and portraits. Here we find examples from the moment of his arrival in Toledo to what might be considered his last work. There is little from the master's Italian period, just as there is only a meagre selection of important works in the other genres that El Greco experimented with from time to time.

It is logical that the city and the surrounding towns where the artist lived and worked for almost forty years should still be essential places to visit for anyone interested in his work. This is true, not only because of the quantity and quality of his paintings, but also because of the altarpieces and the buildings for which they were made. The Cathedral of Toledo still houses the *Disrobing of Christ* and an Apostle series. The Museo de Santa Cruz (with works from several parishes in Toledo) has the magnificent altarpiece of the Immaculate Conception from the Isabel de Ovalle Chapel, as well as the *Immaculate Conception* from the parish of San Román, and many other religious images. In the El Greco Museum, an old Toledan house near where El Greco once lived, an attempt has been made to recreate the atmosphere of the period. This museum is a treasure-house that includes the splendid *View and Map of Toledo,* the altarpiece from the College of San Bernardino, an Apostle series, and several portraits. The three altarpieces and a few paintings remaining in the church of the Convent of Santo Domingo el Antiguo are still remarkable. The Chapel of San José, quite difficult to visit, houses three altarpieces and the paintings in the main one. The parish of Santo Tomé is an obligatory visit, because of the *Burial of the Lord of Ozgaz.* The museum of the Tavera-Lerma Foundation at the Hospital de Tavera (or of St. John the Baptist) has several paintings, including the late *Baptism of Christ* that was commissioned specifically for the hospital. Its church still holds

the structures of El Greco's three altarpieces and a beautiful tabernacle.

Outside the city of Toledo itself, the Hospital de la Caridad in Illescas
houses a fine group of altarpieces in their original setting.

In Madrid, the Royal Academy of Fine Arts of San Fernando has the
Fifth Seal of the Apocalypse, The Lázaro Galdiano Museum has, among
others, one of the few paintings from El Greco's Italian period to be
found in Spain.

At the Monastery of El Escorial we find several works, including the
Martyrdom of St. Maurice and the *Allegory of the Holy League* (or
Dream of Philip II). The Monastery of Guadalupe (Cáceres) now has
the paintings from the former altarpiece of Talavera la Vieja.

Because of the great popularity of El Greco's work at the turn of the
century, and the conditions that made the plundering of religious insti-
tutions easy, his paintings underwent a tremendous diaspora. This is
why so many of his works can be found in museums and collections
all over the world. A large number of significant paintings can be found
in the United States: the Museum of Fine Arts in Boston *(Fray Hortensio Félix Paravicino);* the Art Institute of Chicago *(Assumption* from
Santo Domingo el Antiguo); the Art Institute of Minneapolis *(Purification of the Temple);* the Metropolitan Museum of New York *(Self-Portrait, Cardinal Fernando Nuño de Guevara, View of Toledo);* the Frick
Collection of New York (portrait of *Vicenzo Anastagi);* the National
Gallery of Art in Washington *(Laocoön* and two paintings from the side
altarpieces from the Chapel of San José); the Dumbarton Oaks Collection of Washington *(Visitation* from the Ovalle Chapel); and the Forth
Worth Art Museum *(Francisco de Pisa).*

In Europe: the National Gallery of London (the model for the *Allegory
of the Holy League);* the National Gallery of Scotland in Edinburgh
(Allegory); the Louvre Museum in Paris *(Crucifixion, St. Louis);* the Dres-
den Gemäldegallerie *(Christ Healing the Blind Man);* the Hermitage in
St. Petersburg; and the Statens Museum for Kunst in Copenhagen.

Regarding El Greco's early work — in Crete or Italy — Greece has some
important works: the *St. Luke Painting the Portrait of the Virgin,* the
Death of the Virgin (from Siros), and the *Adoration of the Shepherds,*
at the Benaki Museum in Athens. His *View of Mount Sinai* is in Irak-
lion (Crete). In Italy, there are also a few early works to be found: the
Modena Triptych; the *Christ Healing the Blind Man* at the Galleria
Nazionale in Parma; and the *Boy Lighting a Candle* and the portrait of
Giulio Clovio at the Capodimonte Museum in Naples.

Basic Chronology

1541: Domenikos Theotokopoulos born in Candia, Crete, an island territory belonging to Venice.

1563: Maistro Menegos appears in Candia as a master painter.

1566: Menegos receives permission to sell a painting in Candia.

1568: The painter sends cartographic drawings from Venice to Crete.

1570: Domenico Theotocopuli receives permission to reside in Cardinal Farnese's palace in Rome.

1572: Still in the Cardinal's service, Domenico Greco enters the Academy of St. Luke as a painter.

1577: After a short stay in Madrid, Domenico Greco settles in Toledo and begins the "Disrobing of Christ" and Santo Domingo el Antiguo altarpieces.

1578: Jorge Manuel Theotocópuli, son of El Greco and Jerónima de las Cuevas, born in Toledo († 1631).

1579: Philip II commissions *Martyrdom of St. Maurice* for the Monastery of El Escorial.

1582: El Greco acts as an interpreter in the Inquisition trial of Miguel Rizo Calcandil.

1583: Finishes *Martyrdom of St. Maurice,* which is immediately replaced by another version by the Italian Romulo Cincinnato.

1585: Rents some apartments in the palace of the Marquess of Villena.

1586: Contracts the *Burial of the Lord of Orgaz* with the parish priest of Santo Tomé.

1591: Arrival of his brother Manusso (c. 1530-1604) in Toledo.

1592-93: Writes his annotations on Vitruvius, in which he expresses his artistic ideas.

1596: Commission for the main altarpiece at the College of Doña María de Aragón in Madrid, which he finishes in 1600.

1603: Signs contracts for the altarpieces of the College of San Bernardino in Toledo and the Hospital de la Caridad in Illescas.

1606: Start of the lawsuit filed by the Brotherhood of the Hospital of Illescas.

1612: Jorge Manuel rents a burial vault for the family at Santo Domingo el Antiguo.

1614: Death of El Greco, without a will, on April 7. On April 12, Jorge Manuel begins the inventory of his father's property.

1619: El Greco's remains are removed to the church of San Torcuato in Toledo.

1621: Inventory of Jorge Manuel's property, still including paintings by his father.

Basic Bibliography

ÁLVAREZ LOPERA, José: *El Greco. La obra esencial,* Madrid, 1993.

ARRABAL, Fernando: *El Greco,* Paris, 1991.

BARRÉS, Maurice: *Le Greco ou le secret de Tolède,* Paris, 1910.

BAYÓN, Damián: *El Greco o la estética del rayo,* México, 1989.

BRONSTEIN, Leo: *El Greco,* New York, 1967.

BROWN, Jonathan (ed.): *El Greco of Toledo,* Boston, 1982.

BROWN, Jonathan (ed.): *Figures of Thought: El Greco as Interpreter of History, Tradition, and Ideas,* Washington, D.C., 1982.

CALVO SERRALLER, Francisco: *El Greco,* Madrid, 1994.

CAMÓN AZNAR, José: *Dominico Greco,* 2 vols., Madrid, 1950.

CLOULAS, Annie: *Greco,* Paris, 1993.

COSSÍO, Manuel B.: *El Greco,* 2 vols., Madrid, 1908; Natalia Jiménez de Cossío (ed.): Barcelona, 1982.

DAVIES, David: *El Greco,* Oxford-London-New York, 1976.

EMRICH, Irma: *El Greco,* Leipzig, 1987.

FRATI, Tatiana: *La obra completa de El Greco,* Barcelona, 1982.

GÓMEZ-MENOR, José Carlos: *Vida y obra de El Greco,* Toledo, 1982.

GÓMEZ-MORENO, Manuel: *El Greco,* Barcelona, 1943.

GUDIOL, José: *Domenikos Theotokopoulos El Greco, 1541-1614,* New York, 1973.

GUINARD, Paul: *El Greco,* Barcelona, 1972.

KEHRER, Hugo: *Greco als Gestalt des Manierismus,* Munich, 1939.

KELEMAN, Pál: *Nueva Visión de El Greco,* Buenos Aires, 1967.

LAFUENTE FERRARI, Enrique: *El Greco: The Expressionism of the Final Years,* New York, 1969.

LASSAIGNE, Jacques: *El Greco,* Paris, 1973.

LEGENDRE, M. and HARTMANN, A.: *Domenico Theotocopuli dit Le Greco,* Paris, 1937.

MANN, Richard G.: *El Greco y sus patronos,* Madrid, 1994.

MARAÑÓN, Gregorio: *El Toledo del Greco,* Madrid, 1956.

MARÍAS FRANCO, Fernando: *El Greco,* Milan-Madrid, 1991.

MARÍAS, Fernando and BUSTAMANTE, Agustín: *Las ideas artísticas de El Greco. Comentarios a un texto inédito,* Madrid, 1981.

MAYER, August L.: *Dominico*

Theotocopuli, El Greco, Munich, 1926.

PALLUCCHINI, Rodolfo: *Il Greco,* Milan, 1956.

PITA ANDRADE, José Manuel: *El Greco,* Verona, 1981.

PUPPI, Lionello: *El Greco,* Florence, 1967.

RAGGHIANTI, Carlo L.: *Periplo del Greco,* Milan, 1987.

SALAS, Xavier de and MARÍAS, Fernando: *El Greco y el arte de su tiempo. Las notas de El Greco a Vasari,* Madrid, 1992.

SCHEFER, Jean-Louis: *Le Greco ou l'eveil des ressemblances,* Paris, 1988.

SAN ROMÁN, Francisco de Borja: *El Greco en Toledo. Vida y obra de Domenico Theotocópuli,* Toledo, 1982.

SOEHNER, Halldor: *Una obra maestra de El Greco. La Capilla de San José de Toledo,* Madrid, 1961.

TRAPIER, Elizabeth du Gué: *El Greco,* New York, 1956.

VALLENTIN, Antonina: *El Greco,* Buenos Aires, 1956.

VV.AA.: *El Greco of Crete. Exhibition Catalogue,* Municipality of Iraklion, Iraklion, 1990 and *El Greco of Crete,* Iraklion, 1995.

WATERHOUSE, Ellis: *El Greco,* New York, 1980.

WETHEY, Harold E.: *El Greco and His School,* 2 vols., Princeton, 1962.

General Information on the Prado Museum

EDIFICIO VILLANUEVA
Paseo del Prado, s/n
28014 Madrid
Telephone:
91 330.28.00
Fax:
91 330.28.56
Information:
91 330.29.00
Wheelchair access available

VISITING HOURS
Tuesday through Saturday:
9:00 a.m. to 7:00 p.m.
Sundays and holidays:
9:00 a.m. to 2:00 p.m.
Closed on *Mondays*

ENTRANCE FEES
General Admission   *500 ptas*

Spanish youth card, student card, or international equivalents.
Cultural and education group rates (by advance request)
91 330.28.25)   *250 ptas*

Senior citizens over 65 or pensioners.
Members of the Fundación Amigos del Museo del Prado.
Cultural and educational volunteers   *Free*

Free General Admission Days
Saturdays, from 2:30 p.m. to 7:00 p.m.
Sundays, from 9:00 a.m. to 2:00 p.m.

Coffee Shop
Tuesday to Saturday:
9:30 a.m. to 6:30 p.m
Sundays and holidays:
9:30 a.m. to 1:30 p.m.

Restaurant
Monday to Saturday:
9:30 a.m. to 6:30 p.m.

Shops
Tuesday to Saturday:
9:30 a.m. to 6:30 p.m.
Sundays and holidays:
9:30 a.m. to 1:30 p.m.

HOW TO GET THERE
Metro:
Atocha, Banco and Retiro stations

Bus:
Numbers 9, 10, 14, 19, 27, 34, 37, 45

From the airport:
Airport shuttle bus to Plaza de Colón, then No. 27 bus

General Information about the Fundación Amigos del Museo del Prado
Museo del Prado
c/ Ruiz de Alarcón, nº 21 – bajo. 28014 Madrid
Tel: 91 420.20.46
Fax.: 91 429.50.20
E-mail: famprado@canaldata.es

Office hours:
Monday to Friday, from 9:30 a.m. to 2:30 p.m.